Ros Bayle

Animal F

ACKNOWLEDGEMENTS

Written by: Ros Bayley

Illustrated by: Russell Thomas

Produced by: Lynda Lawrence.

Published by: Lawrence Educational
Unit 21 Brookvale Trading Estate,
Moor Lane, Birmingham,
West Midlands B6 7AQ

©   Lawrence Educational 2004.

ISBN: 1-903670-38-1

CONTENTS

Introduction

We all need a sense of steady beat when performing any task involving sophisticated movement, i.e. when walking, dancing, writing, cutting with scissors, hammering in a nail or drawing. In fact, it is so essential that if someone lacks beat awareness, he or she usually have difficulty with both gross and fine motor skills.

Recent studies have even shown a correlation of beat competency to school achievement that exceeds that of either social class or mother's education, these latter two being the usual predictors of school success. By helping children to develop beat competency we can improve their chances of success.

There are a wide range of ways in which we can help children to develop beat competency, but the more that young children have opportunities to engage in singing, dancing and rapping and play with instruments, jingles and rhymes, the better they will get.

The rhymes in this book can all be chanted to a steady beat, or if you prefer, you can make up simple tunes to go with them. The important thing is simply to enjoy chanting them and to loose yourself in the musicality of language!

Ros Bayley

Ten Dirty Dogs

Ten dirty dogs came knocking at my door
Rat-a-tat, rat-a-tat, knocking at my door.
Ten dirty dogs came knocking at my door
'Till I said, DIRTY DOGS DON'T DO IT ANY MORE!
So they didn't ... but then ...

Encourage the children to think of other things that might come knocking at the door, e.g. Nine knobbly newts.

Who's That Calling On My Mobile Phone?

Ding-a-ling-ling, went my mobile phone
Ding-a-ling, ding-a-ling, all the way home.
It rang and it rang 'till I said, WHO'S THERE?
Then a terrible tiger said, SPEAK IF YOU DARE!

Repeat the rhyme encouraging the children to think of other animals who might have phoned, e.g. a slithering snake.

The Dancing Monkey

I once saw a monkey
with lovely dancing feet
Go dancing, dancing,
dancing down the street.
He danced and danced
and danced 'till he was
dizzy
Then he drank some
pop that was fizzy, fizzy,
FIZZY!

Repeat the rhyme, encouraging the children to think of other animals that might dance down the street.

Four Hairy Spiders

One hot day in the
middle of June
Four hairy spiders flew
to the moon.
They flew all the way in
a big black sack
And once they got there
they never came back.

Encourage the children to think of other
animals that might fly to the moon and
other ways of getting there.

The Gorilla

One day when I was at the zoo
I heard a gorilla go
MOO, MOO, MOO!
So I turned around and I
said to my mummy
My GOODNESS ME
THAT DOES SOUND
FUNNY!

Repeat the rhyme encouraging the children to innovate. E.g. One day when I was in the park
I heard a duck go BARK, BARK, BARK!

The Baboon

A big baboon with a
bright red bum
Gave me a stick of
chewing gum
So I chewed and
chewed and chewed 'till
I dropped.
I chewed and chewed,
and then I stopped.

Ants In My Pants

I've got ants in my pants
and I don't know why
But they make me jump
right up to the sky.
They make me jump and
they make me itch.
They send me flying
round the football pitch!

The Whale

I once saw a whale in
the bright blue sea
And I said MR WHALE,
RATHER YOU THAN ME
'Cause if I was a whale
in the deep blue sea
I couldn't have
ice-cream for my tea!

Pongo The Dragon

A dragon called Pongo
played on a bongo
And he played such a
lovely tune.
It went
BANG BANG BANG BANG
BANG BANG BANG BANG
BANG BANG BANG BANG
BOOM BOOM BOOM

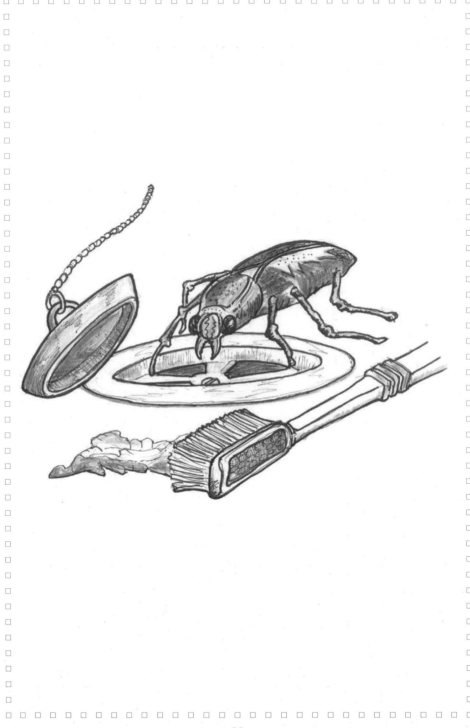

Beetles

We had lots of beetles
in our garden shed
And they got into my
gran's bed
So she moaned and
groaned and kicked up a
stink
'Till they ran away down
the bathroom sink.

A Duck In A Mac

I once saw a duck in a plastic mac.
He swam across the pond going QUACK QUACK QUACK
And I said, LITTLE DUCK GOING QUACK QUACK QUACK
WHY ARE YOU WEARING A PLASTIC MAC?

And he said... *(Encourage the children to think of reasons!)*

One Little Pig

One little pig in a
muddy pig sty
Said, I WISH I WAS A
BIRD AND I WISH I
COULD FLY
'CAUSE IF I WAS A BIRD
AND I COULD FLY
I WOULDN'T HAVE TO
STAY IN THIS MUDDY
PIG STY!

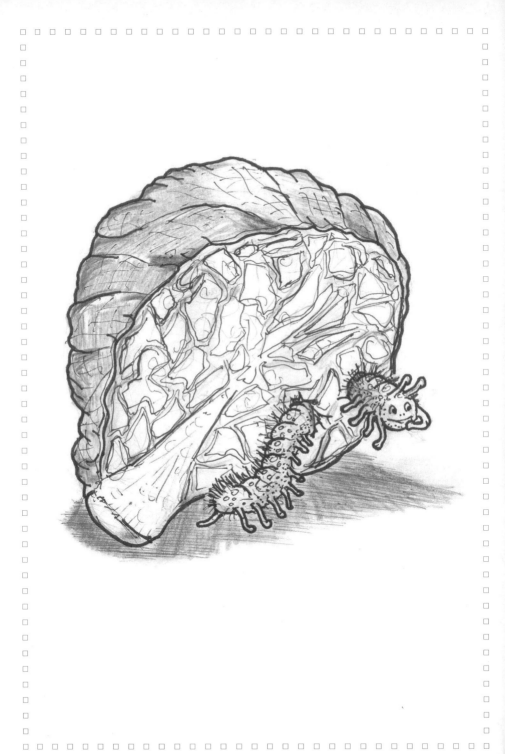

Caterpillar

One little caterpillar,
furry as can be
Said I LIKE CABBAGE
FOR MY TEA
IF YOU LIKE CABBAGE
FOR YOUR TEA
THEN CLAP WITH ME
WITH A ONE TWO
THREE!
One two three, (CLAP)
One two three, (CLAP)
WE LIKE CABBAGE FOR
OUR TEA.

Five Little Birds

Five little birds in a cosy
nest
Said NOW IT'S TIME
FOR OUR BIG TEST
WE HAVE TO LEAVE
THE NEST AND LEARN
TO FLY
WE HAVE TO SOAR
RIGHT UP TO THE SKY
SO FLAP YOUR WINGS,
ONE TWO THREE FOUR
AND MIND THAT YOU
DON'T HIT THE FLOOR!

Fleas

Five little fleas were
jumping on a log
When one of them saw a
very hairy dog.
So they jumped on his
back with a great big leap
And snuggled down for a
cosy sleep
And they stayed for a
week
They stayed for a week
They stayed for a week
In a deep, deep sleep!

The Squirrel

One little squirrel by our back door
Ate our dog's food from the kitchen floor.
He came lots of times, he was so tame
And he made my sister laugh like a drain.

We hope you have enjoyed this rap book.

Other books in the same series are:

Ros Bayley's **Animal Raps** ISBN: 1-903670-38-1

Ros Bayley's **Action Raps** ISBN: 1-903670-42-X

Ros Bayley's **Beanbag Raps** ISBN: 1-903670-43-8

Ros Bayley's **Noisy Raps** ISBN: 1-903670-44-6

Additional rhymes and further guidance on developing children's beat competency can be found in our '**Helping Young Children With Steady Beat**' resource pack.

Included with this pack is a small cuddly toy called BEAT BABY, who can be used at the beginning and end of sessions to help focus the children and to bring emotional engagement to the whole process.

ISBN: 1-903670-26-8

For further details of these and our many other publications, visit our website:

www.educationalpublications.com